Stone Going
Home Again

THE ASSOCIATION FOR
SCOTTISH LITERARY STUDIES

The Association for Scottish Literary Studies aims to promote the study, teaching and writing of Scottish literature, and to further the study of the languages of Scotland.

To these ends, the ASLS publishes works of Scottish literature; literary criticism and in-depth reviews of Scottish books in *Scottish Literary Review*; short articles, features and news in *ScotLit*; scholarly studies of language in *Scottish Language*; and *New Writing Scotland*, an annual anthology of new poetry, drama and short fiction, in Scots, English and Gaelic. ASLS has also prepared a range of teaching materials covering Scottish language and literature for use in schools.

All the above publications are available as a single package, in return for an annual subscription. Enquiries should be sent to:

ASLS
Department of Scottish Literature
7 University Gardens,
University of Glasgow
Glasgow G12 8QH
UK

Telephone/fax +44 (0)141 330 5309
or visit our website at **www.asls.org.uk**

Stone Going Home Again

(NEW WRITING SCOTLAND 28)

Edited by
Alan Bissett
and
Carl MacDougall

Association for Scottish Literary Studies

Association for Scottish Literary Studies
Department of Scottish Literature, 7 University Gardens
University of Glasgow, Glasgow G12 8QH
www.asls.org.uk

ASLS is a registered charity no. SC006535

First published 2010

British Library Cataloguing in Publication Data

A CIP record for this book is available
from the British Library

ISBN 978-1-906841-01-0

The Association for Scottish Literary Studies
acknowledges the support of the Scottish Arts Council
towards the publication of this book

Printed by Bell & Bain Ltd, Glasgow

CONTENTS

INTRODUCTION

To be a writer is to be a focused skiver.

It's not that it isn't hard work. Ask anyone stuck arse-about-face halfway through the long tube of a novel, hauling mechanical bits and sprockets, both start and finish mere pinholes of light at either end, whether or not it feels like a nap. The skiving comes elsewhere. It is attitudinal.

An artist must live at one step removed from everyone else, curiously observing the ebb and flow around them. You have to be close enough to empathise with society, and yet not be consumed by it entirely – Mortgage! Career! Keep the profits coming! Work! Work! – and watch your soul disappear into the office shredder.

Practice for this nimble sidestepping comes in the peculiar lifestyle arrangements needed for writing to happen at all: the flickering laptop once the kids have gone to bed; the frantic scribbling on a dead shift. Alan Warner phoned in sick in order to write *Morvern Callar*. Structured procrastination: avoiding work you're supposed to be doing by doing work you actually cherish.

Focused skiving.

We are fortunate that, in Scotland, structures exist to make this more joyous kind of work possible: the Scottish Book Trust and Arts Council have bursaries and mentoring schemes for writers at any stage in their career, whether school pupil or established poet. A network of writers' groups stretches across the land. The live literature scene is bursting with new talent and relentlessly cross-fertilising with music, film, comedy and theatre.

Conversely, however, actual publication opportunities have dried up. No major Scottish short-story prize currently exists. Literary magazines are dying (although *Gutter* is a new, welcome exception). Mainstream publishers have stopped producing anthologies. The supermarkets and High Street chains, whose stock is controlled by the South of England, are pulping Scottish literature. The only brand they seem interested in is Tartan Noir. A whole culture is slowly being erased. In such a climate, the role of *New Writing Scotland* feels more vital than ever.

So it gives us a feeling of immense responsibility to have stewardship this year, and do our bit to help reward more skiving. Everyone here has downed tools, edged towards a fire exit left carelessly open, whistling as they went, hoping no-one will notice. Just for long enough. That each piece has its own unique hum, its way of recreating the world on its own terms, suggests too the mental escapes these writers have made, which hopefully will inspire readers.

What was most noticeable to the editors this year was the higher quality of poetry than of prose. Many of the poems sang, while relatively few of the stories did. Perhaps mass-market imperatives and the lack of opportunity for prose writers have led to an inevitable blunting of short fiction. The truest voices seem to have fled into the ever-more rarefied sphere of poetry, where such compromising forces as 'the market' are disregarded. It's telling that some of the best prose experiments occupied the miniscule forms of flash-fictions and micro-narratives. Perhaps because of the compression of Scottish culture, the pressure grows stronger within the smallest forms, and a thrillingly different perspective emerges. Not here are to be found patronising *The Scheme*-like stereotypes or pidgin Scots. The country on display in this book is full, linguistically varied, and earthy. Stone going home again.

Meanwhile, the financial sector lurches drunkenly above us, spilling chaos in its wake. It will be interesting to see how the new crop of writers react to the sudden challenge of a Conservative government, what shapes and stances it will force our nation to adopt. Or adopt anew. To start with, some focused skiving might be a good way of rewarding an employer who may soon be firing you anyway. If you're reading this at work, we're already on the right path. These writers, and many of you holding this book now, will form the new movements in Scottish letters, that necessary republic.

Let the focused skiving commence.

Alan Bissett
Carl MacDougall

NEW WRITING SCOTLAND 29

The twenty-ninth volume of *New Writing Scotland* will be published in summer 2011. Submissions are invited from writers resident in Scotland or Scots by birth, upbringing or inclination. All forms of writing are welcome: autobiography and memoirs; creative responses to events and experiences; drama; graphic artwork (monochrome only); poetry; political and cultural commentary and satire; short fiction; travel writing or any other creative prose may be submitted, but not full-length plays or novels, though self-contained extracts are acceptable. The work must be neither previously published nor accepted for publication and may be in any of the languages of Scotland.

Submissions should be typed on one side of the paper only and the sheets secured at the top left corner. Prose pieces should be double-spaced and carry an approximate word-count. **You should provide a covering letter, clearly marked with your name and address. Please also put your name on the individual works**. If you would like to receive an acknowledgement of receipt of your manuscript, please enclose a stamped addressed postcard. If you would like to be informed if your submission is unsuccessful, or would like your submissions returned, you should enclose a stamped addressed envelope with sufficient postage. Submissions should be sent by **30 September 2010**, in an A4 envelope, to the address below. We are sorry but we cannot accept submissions by fax or email.

Please be aware that we have limited space in each edition, and therefore shorter pieces are more suitable – although longer items of exceptional quality may still be included. Please send no more than four poems, or prose work(s) to a maximum of 3,500 words in total. Successful contributors will be paid at the rate of £20 per published page.

ASLS
Department of Scottish Literature
7 University Gardens
University of Glasgow
Glasgow G12 8QH, Scotland

Tel +44 (0)141 330 5309
www.asls.org.uk

Patricia Ace

THE BEST TEN DAYS OF MY MOTHER'S LIFE

She didn't miss home or hanker
after my father's company
or the care of my older brother,
who on visits would cradle me
and call me a doll.
And why would she?
What need has a new mother
of anything but life's most pressing
necessities? Food and water
and rest and every four hours
the nurses carried me to her,
wrapped in a pink blanket,
my fingers searching through holes
like seaweed caught in a net,
and she would breathe
the brackish smell of my skull,
marvel at the dark spot on my crown
pulsing like the centre of anemones.

She read and ate and rested,
watched the grey waves beat the shore,
slept away the crushing tiredness until,
every four hours,
that tingle in her filling ducts,
they carried me to her,
tucked neat as a gift in the blanket
with the satin edge,
my starfish fingers opening and closing
round flesh warm as water,
my cockle mouth locked
to the rock of her breast.

Dorothy Alexander

FOUR BORDERS MICRONARRATIVES

Jenny Corbett wis a clever lassie but her faimily wis pair,
so insteed ae gaun tae the High Schuill she went strecht
intae the mill. The heidmaister pleaded wi her fither, sid
there wid be a bursary (for ee hud tae paye in thae days),
but ae widnae huv it.

Tait's horses strained tae pu muckle cairtloads ae graivel
oot the Tweed. The water drainin oot fairly shushed
an spaurkled; there wid be a trail aw the waye back tae
Bosles. Later on, ae'd bring the horses back for a swim,
an, often as no, ae'd be in aside them.

The washin took aw day. Scrubbed an bleached in water
frae the Shore Well, it wis rozzered on a big yellae stane
on the beach or hung oot on the hedges up the Loanin
an watched in case it blew away or the coos hud a bit
chow at it.

Eyemooth folk were right supersteeshious. Ee daurnae
mention pigs, salmon or rabbits. Meetin a meenister
or a priest, gien onybody onythin oot eer hoose on a
Sunday, hairy weemin an goldfish were aw unlucky. An
ee aye hud tae gaun oot a different door frae the yin ee
came in.

These four pieces, based on recorded memoirs from Scottish Borders Council's Memory Bank, come out of a project that has oral narrative tradition at its core and in which they function as the starting point for experiments in found poetry. They exploit the contention that fifty is the maximum number of words that we as humans can memorise *verbatim* without recourse to the written word.[1]

They are from the memoirs of Jenny Corbett, Willie Brown (*Tait's horses*) and Mark Fairbairn (*The washin took aw day* and *Eyemooth folk*). Bosles is the local name for St. Boswells.

---

[1] I.M.L. Hunter in Rubin, D.C., *Memory in Oral Traditions*, Oxford University Press, Oxford, 1997, p.6.

Kate Armstrong

APPLES

A trace of salt in the air
and a south-facing slope
falling leaves everywhere
I take the back road in hope

of apples. Not to pick, but to find.
This stretch of land was set apart
for orchards, once. Now the road's lined
with brambles, birch and gean. The apples were the heart.

They were bred for early fruit, late flower
and just this soil. Their names are little known –
Tower of Glamis, Bloody Ploughman, Lass o Gowrie –
and they grow. Somehow, they go on.

Few orchards remain, but in rough
land between tidy villages, so smart
with their two-car driveways, there's enough
space for the trees to lurk, the seeds to start

unseen. You need to look. You need to wait.
Stand around. Here it comes, a bit of a breeze
and bright apples roll on tarmac, gold, scarlet,
from the scraggy, almost-hidden trees.

And in the ancient sheds where ladders crumble
and wooden trays decay, pruning-hooks rust,
there are no skilled hands now. These sheds will tumble
soon, un-noticed, and turn to dust.

I crouch over the apples, cup my hand
on myth, on fairy-tale, and lift one to my mouth.
It smells of magic, tastes of nothing known, found
here and now, long ago, salt in the air, facing south.

Jean Atkin

FAMILIAR
for Elizabeth Waugh, sculptor of Eskdalemuir

The hare runs its thin path through her brain
in the small hours, while her body burrows in sleep.
Its hind legs hoop whipcorded through dry grasses.
Its wholemeal pelt is downy to her fingers.

Nights, she perches the racing scarps of its shoulders,
notes the velvet of a black-tipped ear winged back
against her cheek. She thinks she can
        even see the eye's edge,
that limpid bulge of effort, the mottle
        on the amber disc.

She stalks the hareling, the one who
        doesn't go straight home.
Who lopes the electric tracks of her synapses
        to draw the dogs down the hare's maze, away
from the scrape where the leveret
        lies, still and quaked.

She constructs the hare's swerve on wires,
        a frailty propped on a tin.
An eldritch thing, collapsed then lifted, workshopped
into plaster layers. Her hands deal bulk and bone.
Deftly she lines and re-guts her creature.

Now she shaves muscle, files slim
        weight on narrow legs.
She invokes gravity: notes its toes splay, slightly.
One morning it lifts its head, directs its gaze.
She nets it in bronze.

Forbes Browne

RUMMLE

Tay is weest the nicht,
Banff bailies biggen drumlie on the wa heids;
pickmaws flee in tae reest, ticht hauden,
kenning the wather sic cloods bring.

There's mackerel backs i the lift, but the gows
hiv nae thocht o fushin nor meat,
like baldies or fifies they flee
ower Brochty Castle skerries
tae their sicker hythe.

Alow the lowrin lift the firth grues,
wanrestfu wi the onding o the skail,
glockenin an girlin i the immis mirk,
makin mane fur the shored kintra.

For the lan is fykie wi the comin fizz
o glamshach gomerels wha wat
the wanworth o awthing
but naething's wirth:
they crouse cockapenties wha wid reeve
the grund o the fowk
tae bigg their pailaces.

Tom Bryan

POST OFFICE QUEUE, BEFORE CHRISTMAS

Florid, rough, a smoker's cough
she spoke huskily to our nervous line.
'Aye. Fine. Wish I was a bird,
even a wee bird would be enough.'

We smiled shyly at our shoes
as she stubbed her fag out on the floor.
'Aye, if I was a bird, I'd fly up high
then shite doon on the lot of youse!'

She turned, tugged my sleeve.
'Except you son, you're awright'
glowered, then plodded flightless
into the dying light.

E M Buchanan

AGIN MISCHEFE

ab initio

In the crack atween
here an' there
atween the cryin'
an' the kirstnin'

they come

I'll gi'e ye a hansel o' siller
an' a drap o' haly watter

*

midnicht

In the gap atween
noo an' then,
when it's nather
the day nor the morn,
atween the strike
o' the midnicht bell
an' the hearin' o't

they come.

I'll gi'e ye a reid ribbon
a sprig o' rowan
an' the Guid Buik

*

Yule

In the crack
o' the open door atween
the Auld Year an' the New,
atween the ingang an' the ootgang,
when derkness is bool-hornit
an' the nicht is lang

they come

I'll gi'e ye the cream o' the well,
a reid herrin', an' a bairnie
in a byre.

*

Pasque

In the arch o' the heel
an' the toe
o' the sun's daunce,
when bauds gang gyte
an' lift thir lugs abune the rigs
an' ilka lad an' lass
in the bluebell wuids
is in a ree,
in atween the twa lichts

they come.

I'll gi'e ye a rabbit's fuit,
a cup o' wine, some breid
tae brak an' a wuiden cross.

Solstice

When midsimmer-eve
tirls wi' glamourie, an' glimmers
wi' unseen wingit things
that flichter in the trimmlin' air
an' the sun steps
nather back nor forrit,
in the crack in the shell o' time

they come

I'll gi'e ye a bunch o' ferns,
St John's wort
an' three nails o' iron

*

Hallowmas

At the back o' the hairst
when the Carline's cut,
atween the bleeze
o' the Hallow-fire
an' the derk o' midnicht,
when bats flit
an' hoolets scraich,
in the crack
atween plenty an' dearth

they come.

I'll gie ye
a puddockstane,
a puckle saut an' garlic,
an' a paternoster.

*

finis

In the crack
atween the ebb an' the flow
when the caunle burns low,
warm bluid growes cauld
an' yir breith gaes oot
by the open door,
when I lowse the knots
o' yer windin' sheet
tak oot the nails
frae the coffin lid,
an' yer haunds are tume

they will come

John Burns

LAY THE BIG MAN GENTLIE DOUN
for Howard Hann

Lay the big man gentlie doun
He's sleepin nou an winna wake
But lichtlie ye maun lay him doun
Wi hands that yince held his
As he whirled ye an birled ye
Across the spinnin flair
Yet held ye sauf within the circle o his airms
While leadin ye
In yon dance we aa maun jyne.
The fiddler has pit up his bow
The dancers nou are gane
Too suin he's taen but he's sleepin soun
There's nocht but luve remains.
Sae lay the big man gentlie doun
He's sleepin nou an winna wake
But lichtlie ye maun lay him doun
An feel the wecht an ken the worth
O that big man that's gane
Sae lay the big man gentlie doun
Lichtlie lay him doun.

Hazel Buchan Cameron

GOLF BALL

It was a gift
when it dropped at my feet,
I slipped it in my pocket and ran home
to study its dimples – its cool bounce.
Like hunger – curiosity finally won.
I broke through its outer shell:
found an endless reel of rubber
wound tight as corset lace:
on and on, on and on
until a small ball,
soft as an ovum emerged
packed with fluid.

I pierced its delicate blue skin,
wrote across newly cut grass –
the names of my future children.

Chelsea Cargill

RIVER OF SHIPYARDS

Ships arrive in boxes
to be assembled inland,
whalers, pilot-breakers,
diving-bells, floating cranes.

Magnets hold in place
conflicting elements
that are to be fused:
gravity, fate,
the ability to stay afloat.

Toy boats drift in tanks.
Three lines meet
on the drawing-room floor,
water, bow, skylines:
a cargo hold grown
from the inside out,
made up mostly of air.

We feed bread to the birds
and hang ladders from cranes.
Whales and shoals of fish
are outlined in chalk
and cigarettes lit from steel rods.

Seagulls shift off
the pier one at a time
while men wave
high up on the hull.

Timber supports
are hacked away.
Fields shrink
to a river of shipyards.

Jim Carruth

WITNESS

'A voice was heard in Ramah'
                    Jeremiah

and her screams
            through the wall
were like something
I've often heard
            at hay time

when leverets
            lie up
in the long grass
invisible
            to the mower

motionless
            pretending
they're not there
crouched
            as if in prayer
to remain untouched

but found
            by reckless men:

their final cries,
her screams
slice like blades
            through my skin.

USES

a butcher
in the back garden

finishing off his beer
boasts of wars fought

before slitting the throat
of our old boar:

blood gushing into a pail
under blue skies.

Useful animal, the pig

It gives us thick cut ham
succulent sausages,
rashers of bacon,

His words sizzle in the heat.

blood for black pudding
bristles for brushes
leather for saddles,
and footballs and bags

Yes – you can find a use
for every part of the pig

except the squeal

After the bleeding,
the scaldering,
the butchering,

its the squeal,
        that stays

seizing my summer.

Alison L Craig

LIKE CHILDREN

Sometimes they walk single file
through the dawn, obedient as prisoners
who do not know they are free.
Innocent as children too early from bed,
pyjamas askew, eyes rubbed bright.
Come in at my door and stand,
watching open-faced, silent yet.
Like children, sit on a swing at afternoon's end,
kicking dusty legs, one shoe hanging off,
too tired to walk, too hungry not to.
I am glad then of the weight of them
on my shoulder, hot and limp
as freshly poached game.
Like children, they smile sometimes
wide as a dolphin, laugh,
open mouths brimming with stars and ghosts.
Chatter like play-park starlings
on a wire stretched tight across the day.
Often, like children, they tell you nothing,
all tight-lipped artlessness;
I can't remember, they say, but it was good.
Make you shake with fear, hang up philosophies
like veils to hide truth behind.
But sometimes, like children, words
are precise as a snowdrop, flawless as a falling leaf.
So brush your child's hair before bed,
tease out the day, find meaning
in the heavy living silk.

Morgan Downie

HOMETOWN

there, their copper
bell tongues clash
the metal grey
stairwells echo
their orisons out
into the shuttered streets

there, the empty docks
gutted factories, the urn
silence of the machine floor
a night that sings of
ambulances and beatings
furious intoxication

there, the clock glass shatters
blackened pigeons startle
rise like the hopeless
letters of dead men
bunting drags in the gutter
smokestacks glower
silent as crematoria

there, in the bus station
a porter chains the gates
the last buses departed
half empty
carbon monoxide
the stink of diesel
grace notes
to scent their passing

Colin Fraser

ABBA

Fife was mustard cars bustling with gruff men
who spat ambitions into powdered coke,
dreams just lumps of carbon fit for the grate.

His father forbad the pit – it caught you
whole. His gift was clean air, draw himself fresh
to make a fruitful world above the ground.

Work changed with fashion, wood begat metal,
air force begat confidence, travel, spice.
He grew children and cars, tended his wife,
opened up an atlas of shares and homes
while his friends were striked out of livelihoods,
forced to resurface when it was too late.

As his country died, he faced life with pride
and made winters his long celebration
of what had not yet been but waited, cruel
as a lump of coal and just as unfair.

Graham Fulton

THE MAN WHO LIKED TO
TALK ON THE BUS

headlights rain skuze me bit ji no whi thi name uh
thi wee baby in Addamz Famly
     Valyewz iz its goat a daft
wee black mustash ah think heez
     cawed Hubert heez cawed
Hubert am pretty shoor ji no naw nivir mind anyway
whis yir name Debbie thas a nice name
     ur yi married Debbie
whis hiz name Danny DebbienDanny ji want ti
divorce Danny Debbie an marry me
     ha ha naw nivir mind
whir ji work Thi Council thas a joab fur life that iz a
joab fur life if yi dont mess thingz up whiji do a sek
re tarry thas a joab fur life that iz sewz
     dayin a cleanin joab
ur thi buildin trade ji like a drink Debbie whiji
drink gin whiji like in it tonic a wee slice uh lemon ur
lime if they huv it it makes yi sad gin ma famly ma
mother boo hoo ah hope yi dont mind me talkin ti yi
ma palz heedz a bit skrambuld heez
     bin in thi court aw day
an heez really worried he didny day
     it bit av telt him its
no up ti thi judge its up ti thi joory
     thas a nice accent yuv
goat American whirrabootznAmerica New York that
wiz mad that terrurist thing oan thi telly terrurist thas
a joab fur life that iz ha ha nivir mind
     a new sumdy who
came frum New Jerzey ah think he
     Jeezuz heerz ma stoap its bin
dead nice talkin ti yi Debbie bye darlin
     take care headlights rain

John Greeves

SUICIDE

Don't worry if you can't find the spot
where she jumped, black ravens in her mind
winged free, hair blown back,
eyes of brittle glass.

Don't be embarrassed to peer over,
feel the rush of blood to your head,
see the dizzy rock departures far below, or hear
gulls cry, waves pound and hope slip.

Don't think about contorted limbs,
fractured skull, matted hair on stone,
or that sudden thud … bouncing her down,
in somersaults of life and death.

Don't see a face, trickled in blood,
or watch accolades of petal foam sweep her feet.
Don't remember the young girl playing on the beach,
bucket and spade, a smile stretched beyond
the horizon of her parent's loss.

Rosemary Hector

THE NATIONAL THEATRE OF SCOTLAND

No materials. No plaster.
No copper, or verdigris, shaped glass
No argument over bamboo,
The significance of slate.
No architect or topping out
Ceremony, querulous
Opening, official and unofficial
And where will they sit, or stand
And beside whom, and press
And security and trumpets and royalty
Or not and the debate continuing
For ever, about why or why not.
No. Just sinew, sweat, wit.

Norman Kreitman

THE LOVESONG OF THE HERMIT CRAB
A dialogue

'The beach is now deserted, apart from all my cousins
who number several thousands but have gone the other way.
The low sun casts red shadows on the sand,
the wavelets all are waving, the tiny clouds are drifting.
Won't you shuffle off your housing and come strolling
to that rockpool by the strand?'

'I cannot leave my dwelling, there are gulls
intent on supper – the Blackhead and the Whitethroat
and the one I dare not name.
Besides, I am a modest girl, unused to public venturing
and to show my many legs, antennae and appendages
would cause me deepest shame.'

'Your secrets are no secret, for half the crabs in Christendom,
though none of them so elegant, are fashioned just like you,
and the gulls are – at the ceilidh. So let us sidle round, and
      backwards,
as we tango claw to claw.
Then we can feast on mouldy seaweed, and with luck
may find a cockle dead only for some days. We'll wander
in the gloaming, and together count the stars,
and you shall be First Lady of our kingdom by the shore.'

Alexander Lang

GREYLAGS

Wi oot flaa
wrocht frae ae
piece
o seamless
        silk
the loch
an sky

Abuin
a raggit skein
dwindles
tae a raw o buoys
oan the tidal
licht
        knirls
tae beads
lowse
oan a string

Ahin
at illusion's
rim
        it rins
the fabric like
ae bruken threid
syne
invisible

Lis Lee

LOST AT SEA

in arbour a elmsman
steers is sailing boat ard
round a mooring buoy.
e ooks it up on deck,
e looks like e's ad a ard day.
is boat is pretty, illiard,
wooden, traditional,
er transom says 'eavenly maid'.
is retirement plan is to
circumnavigate islands.
is boat secure e tidies up,
I ear im tell is wife
to and im a jib,
is ead pokes out
a foredeck atch.
back on deck, e angs is ead
over er stern, to study
eavenly maid's bobbing butt.
elp! e cries, aitch is missing.

Linda McCann

Extract from SMASH THE GLASS SLIPPER
for Philip Hobsbaum

Chapter One
The Other Woman

March 1990
The first time I was alone with the Mother, she asked how much money I had in the building society and was I a good fuck. I soon learned that she is not always this subtle.

And Baw Heid's a born sister. Maybe she'd be a ward sister by now if she'd carried on nursing. She's standing by her brother in his madness of being with me, ready to forgive him one day for ignoring her warnings. She has that constant air of having rested her case. She's a one-woman silent order.

Sam has changed a lot since he met me, but he's like a house onto which an extension has been built, and his mother and sister insist on using only the original part. Not that your family should have access to all of you, but I see the old Sam being crammed full of their furniture, and, though his windows might rattle now and then, he goes along with it.

Sam's the youngest, and the only one still living, as they say, at home. Sister Baw Heid lives a few streets away, sharing a flat with their brother Paul. He's gay.

The older brother Alasdair is a bank manager in the South Side, and the eldest brother, Iain, lives down in London. He's a lawyer, married, one kid. The family hates Iain's wife, not because she's English, but because she demolished Iain and moved him stone by stone to England.

We'll need to get a place of our own. It's not romantic to share a single bed with something that scratches its balls in its sleep. We could get somewhere for now, for the money the Mother's charging us in rent, since I moved into Sam's room. Wear and tear. It's a new tax, on choosing your own girlfriend.

Regina Crescent is a cobbled curve of town houses facing a row of caged trees which sway like manacled ballerinas. Each entrance is straddled by columns, buckled high in a wrought-iron balustrade. Eyebrow windows watch from under the eaves and, chimneys like muskets, the crescent is always ready for inspection. Nothing deviates. But some days when the sun comes out, the houses take a step back and pick up their skirts of shadow, pillars at ease in fishnet stockings, cast by the wrought iron.

As you step through the door, the staircase slinks back and the chessboard floor gleams so wide that the front doors on either side of the house must have been dummy. The hall fireplace is a black marble proscenium with a crazed hearth where Delft shepherds and milkmaids seem to pop up and do a square dance when the sun shines. The grate exhales a nebula of dried flowers and dribbles bouquets of dust. Every Thursday the cleaner comes and brushes away a new Monet.

My mum had a long hall. Long and so narrow that you couldn't get by when the hall cupboard was open. That press was a jack-in-the-box of clothes for every season, 'a present from' teatowels and embroidered tablecloths with nowhere to go, all packed in like a hanging rag rug.

Sam's room is on the first floor. It always looks burgled. Disembowelled drawers spill onto a floor where shoes lurk like crocodiles beneath clutching shirts, in a stiff undergrowth of peeptoe socks. Up in the corner, a derelict web waits like rows of empty seats in an auditorium. The cleaning lady only does the bathrooms and the ground floor.

My mum used to clean big houses like this, sometimes took me with her. That was before she started the bus cleaning. On stormy winter nights, she'd out on the night shift. She's retired now, but when I'm on a bus, I feel a pull in the quick of my stomach when I see the sticky rolling of a discarded Irn Bru bottle, half-full of urine. You got paid more when there was sick or urine to clean up. Once, there was a legendary big human toley, standing on its end, in the upper luggage alcove – and in the days before the buses were one-man operated.

In Sam's room, I wade through denim puddles with a flotsam of collapsed beercans and twisted, cheese-scabbed pizza boxes. That's men for you. Sometimes it's hard to be a feminist. You can't be houseproud.

On the walls are faded album covers and relics of good nights; street signs with rusted puff-candy corners; boozy barcloths, stiffened like Biggles' scarf, and beermats, swollen like puff pastry. Glazed in yellow Sellotape, torn triangles mark the dark absences of posters, and a rusty tack above the bed dangles a purple fuzzy-felt ticket, 'Big Country, Live at Barrowland'. (Big Cunt, actually. Some letters are scored out.)

A paper Habitat moon hangs low, hideous cocoon for some giant moth, a poisonous blowfish swimming through our sky. But when the lights go out and the ceiling disappears, we have our own universe of glowpaint stars.

Friday. This morning, I walked in on Baw Heid and the Mother, bleaching each other's moustaches. The tableau stared at me. Baw Heid has thick, black eyebrows that meet in the middle, as if someone's been interrupted while drawing a pair of specs on her. They'd been painting their toenails as well, because they had tampons (unused) stuck between their toes. They've all got the same big, pig-ignorant feet, like blown-up rubber gloves. I said lovely morning, and left.

A bit of an atmosphere round the kitchen table tonight. Iain's up from London. He's got to be back for a court case on Monday morning. His wife couldn't come – I don't blame her – and the Mother's angry at not seeing her grandson.

Baw Heid was ploughing her mashed potatoes with her fork.

Iain told us about some graffiti he'd seen in the cells; 'Fuck Mandela, Free me'.

'Plural word that,' said the Dad. 'Singular graffito. Little scratch.'

Alasdair met some English bankers last week in an Ethiopian restaurant, and as the waiter was showing them to their table, Alasdair quipped, 'So what do we do here then? Just sit and not eat for a few hours?'

'Oh he's terrible, isn't he?' said the Mother, and Baw Heid sniggered on cue. But the clients hadn't got it. That was one thing about the Scots – Alasdair shovelled more mince into his mouth – no one could say we don't have a sense of humour.

Iain told us about a man who asked in court if he could pay his fine at two pounds a week, and the judge told Iain, 'Would you please inform your client that this a court of law, not a Christmas club.'

They asked Baw Heid how her job was going. She works for a Gaelic publisher. They've got a Glasgow City of Culture grant to translate the complete works of Enid Blyton into Gaelic. Baw Heid's halfway through *First Term at Malory Towers*.

Yes, Sam was still portering away at the hospital, and things were fine at the gentleman's outfitters where Paul works. No one asked me about my job. They'd heard enough when I was introduced as an English teacher.

Baw Heid and the Mother were asking how much I pay to have my hair done, and why didn't I just do it myself? In case it turned out like theirs. If my hair's not a great advert for going to the hairdresser's, theirs is. They both have that lumpy home perm, bleached the colour of peed snow.

Iain, Alasdair and Paul are at various stages of balding, but Sam and the Dad have manes which sweep back from their foreheads, Sam's black and the Dad's white.

The Mother was going on at Paul because he brought over his new Highland outfit and it's not in the correct tartan. When he cradled it out of its tissue-lined box, you'd've thought he was exhuming an enemy. I had to hide it in Sam's room in case the Mother swung for it once she'd had a few.

Baw Heid didn't take her dessert, but she stayed at the table and doodled down the margin of the *Oban Times*.

The Dad told us the word 'kilt' is of Scandinavian origin, probably eighteenth century.

Baw Heid was drawing daisies, engrossed in the arc of each petal. Sam was scraping steel on Pyrex, polishing off the mince.

'You've got a tartan of your own,' said the Mother.

'Simply not my colour darling,' said Paul.

Wouldn't be mine either – I've seen it.

'But you have no right to wear that tartan,' said Alasdair, 'And Mum and Dad spent all that money to get a new tartan made.'

Their name didn't have a tartan. 'Sneck'. That's the least of its worries, not having a tartan. The Snecks are born-again Gaels, the *nouveau gaelique*.

Baw Heid's petals were sprouting faster, lapsing into tacky frills with burst seams. An inch or two of zigzag, then she laid the pen down, paralleling it to the newsprint.

'Alasdair's right,' she said, 'You're not a – whatever that is.'

'I'm me and I'll wear what I like.'

Sam waved his fork and spoke a mist of mince, something like, 'So you are,' or 'That's right,' but Baw Heid and Alasdair were saying no, it wasn't as simple as that.

Iain and the Dad shrugged.

Finally, the Mother slammed the table with the butter dish. (It broke, but held together with the butter.) She dragged her stare around the faces, freeze-framing their expressions. 'Do you know what "clan" means?' she rasped. Her eyes were bulging like monocles. 'Well, do you? "Clan" means family, that's what.'

Yes, family as in Manson. Clan as in Ku-Klux.

The Mother's palm was bleeding pink butter. A big fuss, Baw Heid and Sam running around, looking for bandages.

Paul said nothing.

Iain said that last week he was defending a man who fell off a roof during a burglary. The stookied leg didn't get him a break and he was given a harsh sentence. He shouted, 'You big bastard,' and threw his crutches at the judge. The judge told Iain, 'Would you please inform your client that this is a court of law; not Lourdes.'

The Dad sipped his tea, told us the word 'tartan' was sixteenth century, probably Old French.

After the dinner, as the daughter and the sons were going about the business of clearing up, I sat with the Dad in the living room. The Dad is always either smoking a roll-up, rolling one, or talking with one long since gone out stuck on his bottom lip, conducting his words. Now, he was making one, stretching the tobacco into the rolling tin.

He spoke quietly. 'You know, I can't be doing with all this tartan talk.'

'Neither can I,' I said.

He harmonica'd the tin as he licked along the edge of the cigarette paper. 'I mean, what does it matter what bloody colours people think you've a right to have on your back?'

'Safety in numbers,' I said. 'Collective responsibilities. It's like governments, football teams.'

His head of hair rose, rounding like the feathers of a snowy owl. He snapped the rolling machine shut and plucked off the cigarette, tight as a lolly stick. As he lit it, eyes closed against the smoke, he seemed to doze. Then he champed the roll-up between his lips, and it ticked and swirled like the tail of a live mouse. He flicked it to the side of his mouth, looked at me with one open eye, and said. 'Yes. Families.'

Saturday. Wearing a short skirt, Amanda slides onto the high stool. She hooks a heel over the spar, crosses her legs and lets the other shoe dangle. My camera clicks. She rubs her lips together and smiles a white, plum lipstick smile. Her almost-green eyes are seeking reassurance. I return the smile, click again.

Her legs are in sheer sahara, with swirlings of hair. She is tall, and sweetly vulnerable. She is my boyfriend.

It's a month now since I took Sam up the town and he waited in the Wimpy while I got him the size ten stilettos in the tall and small. When the assistant asked was I sure that was the size I wanted, it was like having the power of adulthood in a childhood conspiracy.

In Marks and Spencer's, Sam looked at the men's slippers while I got him the tights. Extra-extra large. 'Tights', that household word – all its variations suddenly syllables of unimagined power.

It started when I got the white killer stilettos. They never fit when you get them home. I was rubbing my bunions when I said could he not stretch my shoes. I was joking. I never thought a Scottish man would try on a woman's shoe.

I started to tell him about my Auntie Betty. She worked in a shoe shop for years and when shoes were too tight, she'd say oh I'll just go and stretch them for you, wait a few minutes in the back shop, and the customer always said oh yes that's much better.

He was unlacing his shoes, taking off his socks.

'Never stretched any shoes at all. Just sang a wee song to herself then took them back.'

He stood up and unbuckled his belt. With a clank of pocket change, his jeans fell to the floor and he kicked them aside. He opened a drawer and unravelled a pair of my stockings. He wafted them onto the bed and rolled his sleeves up as he sat down. He hooked a finger into the back of each shoe, dragging them closer. He rolled ivory silk onto one foot and slid his toes into the mouth of a shoe.

'That's a good idea,' I said, 'The stockings can act as a shoe horn.' I knew his foot would never fit, but something made me avoid any crack about glass slippers.

Then the second shoe was on and he kneaded the cream flesh further into the shoes and stood up. His feet were two unbaked loaves in tins, proven high. He reached down and pulled up each stocking evenly, as if he'd done it before, although I didn't think this right away.

I thought it was good that he saw no threat to his masculinity. Then I didn't want him to be embarrassed. Then I thought he was experimenting, a big child, asking me how he felt. His feet looked painful, like the little mermaid's human legs.

His eyes watched me through tousled hair. The look had lost its innocence and was becoming sinister, hair suddenly fluffy, framing his face, cheekbones more defined. More female. My heart did the high jump and I was in a B-movie with no script, at the bit where the woman realises she's in tow with a vampire or a spaceman.

Something was familiar. My memory spun like pictures in a fruit machine, and halted at my schoolfriend telling me about a man who'd watched her on the train. She had glanced over at open trousers and red frilly knickers, and spent the rest of the journey with her face turned to the window, trying not to laugh out loud. I said I would've been terrified, but she said, 'Of a pair of knickers?'

Sam had become the man on the train, with that look. Now, unable to take my friend's attitude or my own, I was stalling, kidding on I was as yet unaware of anything, while I scrambled for how to react. When I noticed the way his shirt was hovering in mid air, all I knew was that I wanted whatever was under it nowhere near me.

I wanted to defend his human rights, to leave him with the assurance that he was a better person for having this extra dimension. I wanted him to be happy, but with someone else. It was fine for the wives on the *Donahue Show*, but now everyone was right and we were a big mistake. Anything we'd had together snapped out like a power cut and my mind was running a torch beam along possible escape routes. I never felt like laughing, but he looked like Buddha on stilts.

Never having told anyone about being Amanda, he had a long chain of secrets. All night we sat, a couple of old chinas, mugs at our feet, coffee steam unfurling as he unfolded his stories of wearing his mother's make-up, or stealing tights from shops – because it was not stockings, but tights he liked, embracing and encasing.

He had no desire ever to take female hormones and no, there was no way that he could be gay like his brother Paul. I already knew all that, but part of me didn't care about the answers, because I was out of this at the first suitable break in the performance.

The next day, I bought him the black courts. Four inch, they are. The clothes were easy. I took up my mum's offer of rich relatives' cast-offs, all size large. My mum was pleased at me seeing sense in the sensible clothes. Sam and I sorted through them. We extracted shoulder pads and put them into bras. I showed him how to sit, how to position his hands. For hours, I made him up in different ways. Of course, there isn't usually time for him to be the full Amanda, so he'll be a sketched-in version with a pair of tights and a jammy mask of lipgloss. The half Amanda.

From the sex shop at the Barras, we got some she-men magazines, full of stranger-than-fiction naked truths. Sam is nervous in case anyone finds them, but I said they'll have seen it all before. He said, 'Aye but no all on the one body.'

On the spike heels, Sam balances between male and female. Amanda certainly is a big woman, the kind of woman my mum would refer to as a hoose side, the kind most people think only comes with an American accent. Sam said I could tell my two best friends about Amanda, but now I wish I hadn't. I think they're jealous that I've got a new friend. Everything boils down to primary school.

The first one I told is a bit of a Stepford wife. We were on our second bottle of wine and I was paving the way, giving her the I've got something to tell you about Sam, but I want you to know I'm okay about it, and she interrupted me and shouted, 'He's a transvestite!' (We were in a restaurant and the waiter gave us a quizzical look.) My jaw had dropped, locking when she said, 'So's Martin!'

Whenever I've seen her since, she backs out of the conversation, saying there's no way Martin would wear make-up or women's clothes, and he only liked the feel of her underwear against his skin, not on it. She never mentions the size twelve red stilettos he spent a fortune on by mail order or that he wears fully-fashioned seams beneath his pinstripes to ease the boredom of the boardroom.

It was my other friend, the one my mum said was the type who'd trip a man up and be underneath him before he hit the ground, who said, 'But you mean he keeps the tights on when you – I mean what does he – and when I said he just hooks the tops of them down under his – she screamed into her hands and didn't want to hear another word.

This opposition has made me protective towards Sam. It must be his female side that makes him so sensitive and gentle. When you think of it, with all we go through with men, it would be great if you could become a lesbian by deed poll. Not that all this makes me a lesbian. We talked about that as well. I can't be a lesbian, because there is the little matter of the willy.

I'm not keen on them right enough. I've always been wary of willies. It's the pregnancy films I saw as a child. *A Taste of Honey, Up the Junction*. Willies give me the willies. The trouble with willies is they've got men on the end of them.

Now I've had time to get used to it, I consider myself lucky. I have a secret friend, so high in her heels that I can hardly reach to back-comb her hair. I love to dress and pose my giant, bendable knee, twist 'n' turn waist Barbie. Let's face it – who ever wanted to play with Ken?

Patricia McCaw

BONDAGER

Lyin' in the bed now, the same bed
as the hind and his wife,
for the bairns' bed's too wet
for sleep, and work too hard,
the next too hard day.

She's keepin' well to her side, her side,
but every night now, he's pressin'
down on the wife all his fierce now,
as if no-one's in the bed but them,
as if it's no-one.

The wife's strugglin', quietly, strongly,
knowin' that she's there, hears now;
and the bondager slides out,
lies in her claes beside the bed,
huggin' the ugly beneath her head.

She's like a dog, a bitch for the huntin',
her breath held forever it seems,
until the hind's done, and the wife whispers
'Peace now,' and her hand dangles,
red-rough and rubbed skin.

And it's touchin', nearly touchin' the bitch's head.
Her face rises and smells sweet the wife's wrist,
sweet now, on her, but back she slumps,
down, down again,
for she'd felt like lickin' it, lickin' it.

Note: An 'ugly' was the head-covering worn by the women bondagers who were 'bonded' to male agricultural workers (hinds) in the Scottish Borders, in the nineteenth and early twentieth centuries.

Stuart Robert Macdonald

THE HOUR HOUSE

Inside the Hour House
the temperature is about average
for the time of year.

It's summer in the kitchen,
clouds are edged in gold
pan-fried in the butter of the sun,

there's rain in the sitting room,
it's night time in the hall
and love is in the air.

In the upstairs bedroom
the stars come out to play,
comets race our pulses but lose.

The clock strikes autumn
in the blue sky tower
gulls flap on the tenth floor

beneath the skein of geese,
whose prow is an imprint of landmarks,
smoking horizontally from the chimney.

Three white horsetails in the twilight sky
resemble mentholated breaths
photographed by frosty eyes.

But the moon is ten minutes
slow in rising up,
with the wind fast blowing

curtains tight, forcing light
inwards and onto
the burrow of wintered sleepers.

A store of nuts
and an ice cream cone,
pots of soup and paddling pools

and an ant in the pantry
with an atom of gold
it cannot spend,

others with tiny weathers
balanced like feathers
on the cold and dripping nose of the air.

Postscript

From the bedroom
the fog is clearing,
we fall asleep on the hay
made when the sun
and our faces were shining.

Ross McGregor

CUP FINAL DAY, 1997

The toon wis empty when ah went tae meet ma mate
It wis cup final day – killie falkirk – up in glesga
We didnae gie a fuck aboot they diddy teams but
Barely luked et aw the buntin an
    flags fleein everywhaur

We went tae wur usual fur a few efternin pints
The place wis deid joost auld wives
    waitin fur thur men
Ah went tae the jukey an pit oan some beastie boys
The barmaid luked et me while dunkin
    glesses intae the watter

Goat us a couple a wild turkeys then
    we fucked off up the toon
It wis roastin fur may an ah could
    smell ma mates oaxsters
He didnae wash much an drank an
    smoked an ate fried fid
It aw sweated oot ae um when it wis
    warm an he wis proud

We bought twelve breaker an went tae the park
Joost some weans an wimmin waitin
    fur the victory parade
Swallied wur cans quick, goat wur taps
    aff an watched the park empty
Crowds an crowds gaitherin up
    towards john finnie street

Ah lay back, ma heid waistit blinkin in the sun
Ma mate stauns up, cumoan he says,
    see whits happenin
Up there where the hale toons cheerin an singin
Thurs only wan team in ayrshire,
    wan team in ayrshire.

Ann MacLaren

FOR BETTER, FOR WORSE

Just a stupid wee fall, but he's broken his hip and for weeks you've had to help him wash and dress and make sure he doesn't walk about without his crutches, and he's bored and bad-tempered so you've been pushing him around the shops and museums in a borrowed wheelchair just to get you both out of the house, and you're exhausted and wish to God one of your big sons would think of coming over to take him out of your hair for a couple of hours or one of their wives would offer to have you over to their place for a meal, but they don't, and you know they never will and they'll find all sorts of excuses if you ask, and you don't know how long you can go on like this. And just when you think it can't get any worse he gets up one morning and his leg's all swollen and hard, so you phone the surgery and they tell you to take him to Casualty, and you sit there for over an hour because there's worse cases than him, and when he's eventually seen by a doctor you're sent somewhere else to sit for an hour to wait for a scan, and after another wait you're told he's got a big blood clot in his leg. So he's given some tablets and an injection into his stomach, he's told to come back in the morning for another one, and he's quite depressed when you get him home so you make him his favourite fish pie but he's feeling sick again, he's always feeling sick these days, and he vomits it up on the bedroom carpet during the night. He won't go out now except if it's to the hospital so he just sits in his chair and worries and you don't like to go out and leave him and a couple of days later what he's worried about happens. He gets a pain in his chest and he's a wee bit breathless so you get him back to Casualty and he's seen right away so you know it's serious, and sure enough, a bit of the blood clot has broken off and got into his lung. So they take him up to a ward and give him an oxygen mask and you sit with him for a while but he doesn't want to talk so you leave him there and tell him you'll be back at visiting time. You

know you should go into town for some retail therapy or go
and get your hair done or treat yourself to a skinny latte and a
blueberry muffin, but you just go home and have a good cry
and scrub the kitchen floor, and you make an apple crumble
to take to him in case he doesn't like the hospital food. And
he looks better when you see him at visiting and the doctors
must think he's better because the next day they let him out
and he looks quite cheerful till you're helping him into the
shower at bedtime and he suddenly starts gasping for breath
again and you've to phone for an ambulance and while you're
waiting he tries to talk about his will and tells you he's sorry
and he loves you and you tell him not to be so daft because
you're trying to keep it together because you don't want to
think he might be dying and you don't want him to think
he's dying. And they keep him in for longer this time and
he's kept on oxygen but he doesn't look very well and he's
running a temperature so they give him antibiotics and he
begins to breathe easier and you do too, and he begins to
walk about the ward without his crutches, though it's left
him with a terrible limp. Things can only get better you say,
but they don't because the blood tests they've been doing in
the hospital show there's something wrong and the doctor
wants to send him for another scan, a full body one this time
because anyway, he shouldn't have broken his hip, a man of
his age, so you both wait and worry for a few days but avoid
talking about it at visiting time and he gets the scan done the
day before he's discharged and you both sit at home waiting
and worrying again, scared to go out in case the doctor
phones with the result, but it's his secretary that phones and
she says the doctor wants to see you both together and she
says nine o'clock the next morning, so you both know it's
bad news but he doesn't want to talk about it and you're glad
because you don't know what to say and when you get to
the hospital in the morning and the doctor calls you both
in you're not surprised when he says the C word, and it's in
his bones and they'll do all they can but when you get back
outside you're shaking and you want to scream but you see
the tears running down his cheeks and you know you'll have

to pull yourself together for his sake but you wonder just how long you'll be able to keep it up and who the hell will be around to catch you when you fall.

Hugh McMillan

A SUNNY DAY

Leaves scoop up light, spill
some to burn in puddles
or the blunt fretwork of twigs
where birds chuckle and twitch.

The sun has come
like some forgotten cousin
looking for a bed and a lift
early tomorrow to the airport.

We will probably react
with 40 cans of Export
for the price of 36. Then,
in the cool of the evening,

skulls will be gently split,
as the Nith lies languid
as hammered gold,
and it will all end as it started,

a sudden lurid surprise
in the grey slate of sky.

Kona Macphee

INLAND

There's a river, but here's a long haul
uphill from its pebbly burble. A cold spring
threads the stepped streets, over, under,
pooling in a neighbour's garden, lipping,
spilling back into a pipe. When gutters fill
with storm-wash, skimming cars cast ankle-waves
at walls that harbour sodden gardens.
Daily in the square, gulls shark
and bicker round the carrion of lunch
while lorries moor at High Street shops
and crewmen ferry wares. The stopping edge
of town is thin and final as a strand;
beyond it, pylons float, tied buoys becalmed in seas
of barley, haygrass, sheep-cropped choppy stubble.
At nightfall, every full-moon streetlight
dons its yellow glare; there are no tides.

Jason Monios

ON SEAFIELD ROAD

On Seafield Road the tarmac splits like shale,
aghast at horrors risen in its name.
A walled-in trench of tiring buildings:
industry, residence and motorway.

The road itself a byword for one thing,
two things now that roadworks spread unchecked.
Or three things, looking at developments
of bricked-in flats, of eyeless sores.

An artery, this road, a means of leaving
from a corner of an ancient city
to a rolling sediment, pastureland yellow and sere,
past the power works to Seton Sands,
not Bannockburn but Prestonpans.

On Seafield Road, a gap between our pasts.
Old factories, old industry at last
brought low, to hulk and heave no more
until a redeveloper should call.

On Seafield Road, a transport corridor.
How long till it is home to high-rise offices
and flats for those whom industry excites.
Trendy shops, al fresco cafés playing in the traffic.

Undecided stretch of city land,
torn between conflicting needs and uses,
unguided by a central plan or policy,
a council long adrift on sheets of glass,
concrete and far-from-stainless steel.

On Seafield Road, the road itself lies tired,
the buildings left to chisel their own destiny.
Left to find their way, to find a price themselves
when gentry call to colonise Leith Links.

The future of this passage undecided,
waiting for the council's brown bag policy.
The will of the developers made known,
the ancient ceremony by which the deal is made:

the backhanded envelope under the table.

Theresa Muñoz

HARD TO REALLY KNOW

what it is
you are thinking
in the early light

hard to guess
what first thought of the day
makes you rise

and grimace, mouth curling

*

outside the grass shines
January thriving

I don't want to leave you

I mouth generously, pouring coffee

*

inside our relationship
another one
your old one

still with us
in the odd conversation
or photo

and what you have kept –

cake tins, pink sheets
a slick metal wok
grown dusty in the kitchen

*

hard to guess
how far in your mind
you have come

out of the past and into the present;

*

do you remember what I asked you
when we met
at the top of Calton Hill?

I said, do we like
the same
things?

evening light fell
on the smooth planes
of your nose, eyelids and cheeks

*

on the train with you
passing clipped fields
crumpled beaches

the sky clear for the first time today
and both of us riding backwards

into it, glancing sideways
nowhere ready
to talk about it

RELEASE

on the beach
in winter

studying the horizon
mountain fog ocean

*

zippered to the chin
hands curled under my jacket

a moment
in the brief sun,
believing you're here again

*

do you remember
that first snow of the season

the car made
tiny clicks
up the mountain

I pulled two sweaters over my head
stay warm in layers, you smiled

*

where do people go when they're gone?
I asked myself when you died

and I didn't go out at night

preferring
the bedroom's cold glow
the swollen candles, the vague shadows

                              *

anchor on the stone
meaning
someone who was strong

your face after exercise –
lined pink, glowing
moist around the temples

                              *

need to keep telling myself
you're really gone

nowhere near
me, that distant grove of trees
or these battered logs

heavy striped stones clack noisily

as I walk back to my car,
looking around

Donald S Murray

WEAVING SONG
in remembrance of Angus Murray, 1922–81

Dad used to fill the room with praise
these hours spent bowed above his loom,
precenting over patterns, weaving belief
deep into both weft and warp
till wool was flecked with psalm
as each song shuttled, threading verse
through two-by-two or plain
until his finished tweed retained

rhythms of *Kilmarnock*, *Stornoway*
deep within the tightness of the cloth
for a stranger to put on, unaware how faith
was sewn within the garment; bright stitch
among both checks and herringbone;
an active work of worship, prayer
with which my father laboured to prepare
fabric fit for other souls to wear.

WAULKING SONG

'No child of mine will ever have to dip
her hands in urine,' Mam used to keep
speaking of her younger days when she
mucked out byres, waulked piss-drenched tweed
stretched upon a table, a tug-and-pull
to make wool fit for the full tug and pull
of weather, with women weaving songs together,
chanting nonsense rhymes, creating words and sounds
to help keep time with their labour,
neighbours' voices entwining from croft-houses all around

'No child of mine...' And yet I'm forced to keep
changing sheets, the fine bed-linen of one whose sleep's
disturbed by urges that leave him steeped
in urine, wakened nightly by alarms
and soaked pyjamas, and I long these hours for songs
that might assist me in my labours, some neighbours who
will chant out Gaelic incantations, songs and airs
to keep at bay the idiocies of ageing,
the warp that's woven in us by the tug and pull of years.

GHOST WEAVER

Some nights he will rise from his grave on the machair,
brushing the weight of sand from arms and shoulders
before returning to his old loom-shed
to work upon a tweed left there
the day breath stilled and flesh grew cold
and weave a winding sheet for the freshly dead

who had joined him below the ranks of stone
alongside his, knowing they, like him
would feel the chill of being without loved ones
and needed the clasp of herringbone
or fleck to comfort them till they lost their need for home,
folded up like finished cloth set for the mill
          when work on it was done.

John Murray

STONES

Basalt
grand hexagons
make a geometry of six,
Fingal astray

Chalk & Flint
dried blood
as black as lacquer,
the geisha's face

Conglomerate
yesterday's porridge
gone hard in the drawer,
an empty house

Lewisian Gneiss
birth lines winding
in an endless galaxy,
the old man's face

Limestone
pavements
dissolve in the rain,
those empty questions

Mica
white crystals
encrypted in granite,
heart broken

Sand
quickly through time
even as glass,
a window on God

Sandstone
infinite floor plans
forgotten,
many beds unmade

Schist
silver half seen,
half grasped in the streambed,
that secret wish

Slate
split leaves
paper the rafters,
pages turn

Catherine Orr-Frier

ECLIPSED

Tea in the Deanery garden
sunshine and the dim marquee
hats, chat and strawberries.
An interesting couple:
bony schoolboy of a man
still floppy-haired at sixty.
She, his precious flower, adored
face pansy-wide, lips pouty.

He, a talented pianist.
She sketched and painted (mostly oils).
His consonants were crisp, precise
angled like his facial planes.
Fruity vowels round and rich
ripened on her plummy lips.
My Scottish notes seemed crude and gruff
unpolished and ungainly.
Suddenly, not interesting enough
I muttered an excuse
and sidled off.

Jane Patience

TIDE TREIDS

My bairn's on the strand,
daunderin the glim whaur
reamin waters land,
raikin as the pebbles pauchle,
gaitherin razor, clam an cockle.
She hurdies them like smuirichies in a pail,
then lowses them tae the great weet draig.
All her wantins settin sail.

I watch frae the scaur,
see the hievens heich
that raxes hyne awa.
Chitterin souch blaws ferlie throu me.
Gif whan we're fuir we lea wur meirk,
a myndin on this emerant laund…?
She vaigs oot ower the blinterin raw.
Here's ma fit-dunt in the saund.

Walter Perrie

STONE GOING HOME AGAIN

Stone going home again to stone;
poor helpless house, your heart is ash,
bone-shelter of this country's bone,
abandoned arteries, old Perthshire flesh,
stoor smothers every good Scots word.
Ghosts, who, though the roof-beam falls,
who brought you sheep and the shepherd,
speech and song, still prowl your walls.

Only the rowans they planted
keep them out. Only from haunted
sky and wood their silence to your silence calls –
now only the wild birds; starling, mavis, rook,
brown wren that through the thicket moves,
and buzzard *piaow* and pheasant croak,
and the untranslatable noise of doves.

Wayne Price

AT THE GATE, ARIZKUN

The chickens scratch behind the wall;
skinny hens, red-feathered, identical.

Their clucking seems the soft misfiring
of summer's idling engine.

I watch them criss-cross their yard;
the white gate is open wide.

They cross and cross in twos and ones.
They stoop and peck at nothing, nothing.

They never tire; they're never filled.
Their yard is parched, the Basque hills

are tall and green beyond, and there
is only repetition here, but they are

no more restless than the stones
they scrape and tap in the sun.

There is nowhere they would rather be:
the gate is open; they never leave.

In the shade of a pavement café-bar
I light another cigarette, drink another beer.

On the walk here the folded hills
repeated Perthshire; Wales. A scallop-shell

in stone; a white village of beehives;
five woodpiles, all alike, by the roadside.

The chickens scratch behind the wall,
never tired, tired, tired of it all.

with quiet restraint, while he outlines this flesh
he has forsworn to cleave to evermore.
This is his ultimate command: to sit.

By day I pose upright as his canvas
blossoms with pink, a tender portrait of
the painter's wife, meek face and docile eyes
amidst the lace and ribbons of her dress.
In private, his decrees are whispered low,
each dictate met with full obedience.
Oh no, he shall not – though he may paint kings –
tempt me into a slattern's disregard;
I will comply with each request, each law,
in honour of the vows I made to God.

Karin Slater

SOMETHING ABOUT DAD

made him want to be someone else.
On a sunny day when I was wee
I'd sit on the bench at the side of the house
and he'd do funny walks the length of the paving,
one way with his legs apart like Norman Wisdom,
then come back, knees to the ground like a crab.

As a teenager we'd cycle the single-track
down to the beach at Swainbost.
One time he wore a white hardhat,
a find from a previous trip to the dunes,
the plastic strips inside making it too narrow
so it moved sideways on top of his head.

We stopped in the middle of the machair,
and he told me to take a photo.
While I unclipped the camera case
he pulled a piece of black electrical tape
from the front brake cables,
and wore a square moustache.

I was to make sure I got him on centre.
I raised the silver-edged box,
looked through the lens as I can now,
light sky and short grass, no sign of the beach.
He was right in focus,
until he drew his hand to become Hitler.

Michael Stephenson

LANDING

A night-time descent into Glasgow –
thudding through thick banks
of rain-laden cloud, you took my hand
and stillness gathered round us like a ring.

Then we had passed through, drifted
into clear and silent air. Below us,
the city lights were scattered like seeds
glowing in the dark earth, waiting.

Gerda Stevenson

TIME AND SPACE

The full moon
pins us in its circle
as we meet
in the kitchen hallway,
each on some small
domestic mission.

I turn off the light,
the better to see us,
husband and wife,
held between walls
by the night's pure beam,
the journey we've made
through decades
to this moment,
a mere blink
of that cold eye.

Jim Stewart

GAS GIANT

No plumbing these deeps;
no putting a figure
on the weight of methane
in its drowse.

Airs arrange themselves
in the stripes and spots
of bright cyanide vortices
rapt in their swirl

which have forever
to traipse in slow circles
this way and that way,
clockwise and anti,
the cold fogs of their colours
tumbled at leisure.

It obeys nothing less
than a star,
its meekness silent,
the core unreachable.

How it deliberates,
imposes its edict
on anything passing,
gone in its truth,
around which all else
roams at command.

Judith Taylor

THE END

When the long nights returned, the staff absconded
leaving all the plate and the cutlery
unpolished. Dressed in one of your less-
difficult gowns, you roamed the empty halls
and for the first time
went down to the lower levels

where you opened bottles of apricots
and ate them with your fingers, trying to guess
if the pantry held enough
to last you out, and thinking
– to your own surprise, nostalgically –
of bread, and your bowl of chocolate.

Your diversions failed you one by one.
Ignorant how the lamps lit,
you broke your bobbins making lace
on the terrace under the moonlight
and your spinning-wheel – a toy
of gold and whales' ivory – soon jammed.

The clavier lost its tune;
the books in the library repelled you
with their odour of near decay.
At last there was no more to detain you.

The grooms had taken the horses
when they went – an act of mercy,
since you had no idea how to feed
or saddle the things – so you walked away
wondering if you were too late

to learn about the world.
And for the want of a better instrument,
your last act as a Princess
was to take off one embroidered satin shoe
and use the fine heel
to smash the ice on the fishpond.

Valerie Thornton

SOLITAIRE

One wet Easter in Largs,
so long ago that I was young
enough to be there too,
he spent the whole holiday
hunched over a solitaire set
placing and picking pins over

and over, and scribbling ciphers.
By the end of the week,
he had calculated and recorded
the least number of moves
to leave the last pin
alone in a centre of emptiness.

He taught me his elegant sequence
of little leapfrogs and,
for a time, I could flourish it,
but it wasn't big and quick,
like wheelies or cartwheels,
and no-one envied me.

I can recall the opening jumps,
how to clear only a quarter,
before I stagger and stumble.
Among these faded papers,
perhaps I'll find a cryptic record,
and solace in our solitaire.

Ryan Van Winkle

ODE FOR A RAIN FROM DEATH ROW

The rain is a cold, clean prayer,
the only light I want to see.
I say it still rains on her

like it rains on the bars and streets
somewhere outside the walls.
And in the rain, she is always twenty,

her shoes always candy-red Converse,
her jeans always damped to her thighs,
her mouth never parted from mine.

She hasn't pressed her lips to glass
since the fire; the ashes are back to ashes, the dust
follows dust, the spring rain powders her arms

and evaporates in the stare of the sun.
And this rain is the only light I want to see.
A mist that kisses till my socks are sponge,

till the fire fizzles and baby is back again
cooing with hot-chocolate-warm hands.
Before I die I want to stand outside,

birth-naked, let the lord soak me.
But options and pardons are gone.
The priest only offers a glass where

my throat wants a holy rain that pours
in sheets and hoods and lasts for forty days,
till it floods, and floats my sins away.

*'My dearest wish before I die is to stand outside in Scottish rain
and to feel it soak me.'* – Kenny Richey, Death Row, Ohio

Fiona Ritchie Walker

ENCOUNTER, 1979

We met in Amsterdam,
his Irish vowels, my Scots lilt,
discussed the cheapest all-day travel,
ate erwten soup in the youth hostel café.
He bought me a banana.

Someone started the passport game,
mugshots shared. He didn't join in.
When I walked from the girls' dorm
for a midnight wee,
he and a man I'd never seen fell silent.

That night a crowd gathered round the television.
A Dutch suburban street.
The British diplomat's car.
In the hostel café,
an empty seat.

REMEMBERING MARY FLORA

I

You were making little use of the degree
you'd taken in the Celtic languages
at Glasgow University (where you
achieved the highest standard possible)
when I saw you sitting at a table
in Ord House Hotel, in Skye – the great island,
your two hands dirty, bloody with the fish

II

you were preparing for the frying-pan.
Your knife was swift and sharp as you worked
at separating the guts from the rest,
the other parts of the fish that were fit
to be cooked and served up on a dish
before the guests in the hotel. Your keen mind
was every bit as sharp and just as quick

III

as it guided the blade and when it stooped
willingly in order to attend
to the work of the kitchen in your charge.
Although you had been brought up in the house,
and had spent most of your childhood there,
you'd been born in Talisker, and so
the other children used to laugh and tease

Christopher Whyte

A' CUIMHNEACHADH MÀIRI FIONNGHAIL

I

Bu bheag am feum a bha thu dèanamh dheth,
an ceum a thug thu mach sna cànanan
Ceilteach aig Oilthigh Ghlaschu (far na bhuidhneadh
na b' àird' a bh' ac' a dh'inbhe leat) an uair
a chunnaic mi nad shuidhe thu, aig bòrd
taigh-òsta anns an Òrd, san Eilean Mhòr,
do dhà làimh salach, fuilteach leis na h-èisg

II

a bha thu deasachadh airson na h-aighne.
Bu sgiobalta 's bu gheàrrtach i an sgian
rinn am fuidheall a dhealachadh bho chàch,
bho na b' iomchaidhe is na b' fheumaile
a bhruich, 's a shuidheachadh fa chomhair aoigh
air truinnsear anns an t-seòmar-bìdh. Cha robh
na bu lugha a sgiobaltachd 's a ghèiread

III

fiosrach aig an inntinn rinn an lann
a threòrachadh 'na h-obair, is a lùb
gu deònach gus gach uile chùram meanbh
a thachair rithe anns a' chidsin. Ged
a chaidh do thogail is t' àrach san taigh,
rugadh tu ann an Talasgar. Bhitheadh
a' chlann a' magadh ort anns an raon-chluich'

IV

you in the playground alongside the school
when you were a little girl because
they didn't recognise your different accent.
When I first met you, the joints in your hips
had one by one already grown so weak
and shrunken that despite the patient toil
of all the doctors you couldn't get around

V

without the help of a Zimmer frame.
All through the summer that I spent with you,
washing dishes, filling the machine
and emptying it again, paying special
attention to the glasses, making sure
that all of them had a bright, perfect sheen
(they had to be without mark or blemish,

VI

like the mirror in which I would look
every day at the top of my head
worriedly as I saw that the hair
was growing ever thinner, though I was
only twenty-two years old) you could
be found between the cooker and the worktop
but for an hour or two each afternoon

IV

ri taobh na sgoil', is tu nad chaileig bhig,
a chionn 's gu robh blas diofaraichte, neo-
aithnicht' air do chainnt. An uair a chuir
mi eòlas ort, bha fear seach fear de dh'altan
do shlèistean air fàs lag is crìon a-cheana,
's a dh'aindeoin saothair nan dotair uile
cha bhiodh tu gluasad gun chobhair structair

V

mheatailt ris an canadh duine "zimmer".
Air fad an t-samhraidh sin, a chuir mi seachad
a' nighe thruinnsearan, a' lìonadh inneil
's ga fhalmhachadh a-rithist, a' toirt aire
speisealta gu dè cho boillsgeach 's cho
trìd-shoilleir is a dh'fhan na glainneachan
(oir b' fheudar dhaibh a bhith gun sal, gun smal,

VI

mar an sgàthan sam b' àbhaist dhomh sealltainn
latha seach latha air mullach mo chinn,
fo iomagain do bhrìgh 's gu robh am falt
a' sìor fhàs nas gainne, is cha robh mi
ach dà bhliadhn' air fhichead a dh'aois), bha thu
ri do lorg eadar an cucair 's am bòrd,
ach uair no dhà san fheasgar, nuair a bhiodh

VII

when you would be resting in your bed.
The space given to you was narrow, cramped,
the only room you had to operate.
Although I came to Skye to learn the language
the three of you – your sister, you, the maid
– could not speak Gaelic when I was around.
I would hear it a minute or two

VIII

after I'd left the kitchen, at my shoulders.
It wasn't suspicion or mistrust
that left you shy but reticence, training
and diffidence; at least that's how it seemed.
Perhaps that was the reason behind
the formal Gaelic lessons you would give me
each night after dinner. Your sister made

IX

desserts that were so sweet, so overwhelming
that no one was able to resist
the devilishness of their charm – the aim
of her labour was obvious from her size.
Your sister's conversations on the phone
with your brother's wife were long, exhaustive,
Gaelic and English all mixed up together

VII

tu leigeil t' analach nad leabaidh. Bha i
cumhang agus caol, an fharsaingeachd
a thugadh dhut airson do dhèanadais.
Ged a thàinig mi air sgàth na cànain,
dh'fhairtlich air an triùir dhibh, air do phiuthair,
a' ghruagaich is ort fhèin, Gàidhlig a bhruidhinn
'nam làthair. Chluinninn i mòmaid no dhà

VIII

an dèidh dhomh 'n cidsin fhàgail, air mo chùl.
Cha b' e mì-rùn no amharas a bha
'na adhbhar aig bhur diùid, ach fiatachd,
gnàthachas is tàmailt, tha mi creidsinn.
B' ann a thaobh sin, is dòch', a bheireadh tu
leasanan oifigeil Gàidhlig dhomh
às dèidh na dinnearach. Rinneadh do phiuthair

IX

mìlseanan cho mealltach, tàlaidheach
's nach do shoirbhich le neach sam bith seasamh
ri diabhlaidheachd an t-seun' aca. Bha brìgh
a dìchill follaiseach am meud a cuim.
Bu fhada, iomlan, mìon-phuingeach gach còmhradh
's i bruidhinn air a' fòn ri cèil' ur bràthar,
Gàidhlig is Beurla air am measgachadh

X

in such a strange manner, each word from one
language followed by one from the other.
In the mid-morning when we sat down
to have a cup of tea the maid would give
a full account of the state of the sheets
in the rooms she had been busy cleaning
particularly if a young couple

XI

had slept there. As for you, you would find out
about all the ceilidhs and the dances
that were being held at night in Sleat
or further afield, and who could give
me a lift in the car. When I came home,
however late it was you would be waiting
in the kitchen, in your chair and I

XII

would reel off the names of all the girls
I'd danced with. You'd remember a father,
who had been uncommonly religious,
or a grandfather who'd farted so loudly
in church, right in the middle of the service,
that people had never stopped talking
about it to this day. I listened to

X

air dòigh cho neònach leò 's gun deach gach facal
a leantainn le facal bho chànain eile.
Aig meadhan na maidne, nuair a shuidh sinn sìos
ri cupa tì a ghabhail, bhiodh a' ghruagach
a' toirt dhuinn cunntais làin air staid nan anart
leapa anns na seòmraichean a ghlan i,
gu sònraichte nam bitheadh paidhir òg

XI

a' fuireachd annt'. Bhiodh tu faighinn a-mach
gu dè na cèilidhean 's na dannsaichean
a bha gan cumail leòtha ann an Slèit'
air neo nas fhaid' air falbh, is cò dam b' urrainn
mo thoirt leis anns a' chàr. 'S mi tighinn dhachaigh,
air cho anmoch 's a bhitheadh, bha thu feitheamh
anns a' chidsin, 'na do shèithear, 's dh'fheum mi

XII

ainmeannan nan caileag innse dhut
a dhanns mi leotha. Chuimhnicheadh tu athair,
a bha 'na phearsa anabarrach cràbhaidh,
no seanair a rinn braidhm cho gleadhrach, mòr
anns an eaglais, aig àm na seirbheise,
's gu robh na daoine bruidhinn mu dheidhinn
gu ruig an là an-diugh. Dh'èist mise riut

XIII

you no less carefully when you spoke
at length about the witchcraft performed
by the old woman from Mull who once lived
in the bothy down beside the shore
now used in summer by an elderly
English couple. Shortly after that,
you gestured to me as I was waiting

XIV

on tables and you whispered in my ear,
that the woman I could see sitting
by the window with her family round her,
everyone of them looking so ordinary,
was in fact the witch's granddaughter.
You also told me that incest happens
in Harris regularly and said, laughing,

XV

that my hands were so soft and so fine,
I should work as a gynaecologist.
On one day, when the conversation
in the kitchen in the morning turned
to those who go through operations
to change their sex, you had plenty to say,
many opinions and points of view

XIII

cho furachail 's a rinn nuair thug thu cunntas
làn air a' bhùidsearachd a rinn a' chailleach
Mhuileach, bha fuireachd uaireigin sa bhothan
shìos ri taobh a' chladaich, a chaidh a-nis
'na fhàrdaich shamhrachail aig paidhir aosta
Sasannach. Beagan ùine às dèidh sin,
thug thu soidhne dhomh, 's mi frithealadh

XIV

san t-seòmar-bìdh, is thubhairt thu 'nam chluais,
an cagar, gur e ban-ogha na buidsich'
a bh' anns a' bhoireannach a bha 'na suidhe
ri taobh na h-uinneige, le teaghlach uile
mun cuairt oirre, 's coltas cho gnàthaichte
air gach neach dhiubh. Dh'innis
       thu dhomh cuideachd
gun tachrar ris a' chol ro thric sna Hearadh

XV

is thubhairt thu, 's tu gàireachdaich, gu robh
làmhan cho finealta orm is gum b' fheàrr
nan robh mi 'g obair mar lèigh-eòlaiche
nam ban. Air latha àraidh, nuair a b' e
cuspair còmhradh na maidne anns a' chidsin
na bhios 'g atharrachadh na gnè a th' ac'
le opairèisean sònraicht', thàinig pailteas

XVI

came out of your mouth. Because of that
I don't believe it would have bothered you
if you had known about the difficulties
that bothered me throughout that summer.
When a young driver came to deliver
all of the provisions that we needed
in his lorry, and lingered a while,

XVII

I couldn't get his fair hair, or the slim
but strong rise of his neck out of my mind
until I had the chance to calm myself
in my bed in the afternoon. Ewen,
the electrician, gave me the same trouble,
because then I had still not understood
the true inclination of my desire.

XVIII

You found something in me you recognised,
though I'm not sure I know even today
the real nature of our affinity –
a sharpness of mind like your own, or a cool
and foreign look on everything around you,
that unseen detachment that came
because of all the strength of your great mind

XVI

a bharailean 's a bheachdan bho do bheul.
Air tàillibh sin, cha chreidear leam gun rachadh
do bhuaireadh, nan robh fhios agad ciod e
an seòrsa thrioblaidean a rinn mo phianadh
air fad an t-samhraidh. 'S dràibhear òg a' fantainn
car sealain anns a' chidsin, bhiodh a' giùlain
gach lòin a bha dhìth oirnne leis 'na làraidh,

XVII

dh'fhairtlich orm fhalt bàn, is èirigh cumhang
ach neartmhor amhaich luim, a chur à m' aigne
gus am b' urrainn dhomh mo chiùineachadh
leam fhìn 'nam leabaidh feasgar. Bhitheadh Eòghann,
an dealanair, a' cur an aon dragh orm,
bho nach robh aomadh àraidh mo nàdair
fhathast ga làn-thuigsinn leam. Lorg thu

XVIII

rudeigin annam a bha thu 'g aithneachadh,
ged nach eil mi cinnteach, eadhon an-diugh,
gu dè an cleamhnas, am b' e gèiread inntinn
coltach ri na bh' agads', air neo sealladh
coigreach, fuaraidh air gach rud mun cuairt,
an sgarachdainn do-fhaicsinneach a thàinig
mar thoradh air gach feart a bha nad inntinn

XIX

and of the character that caused our kitchen
to grow larger, expand, broadening out
whenever you were sitting with us.
Perhaps you only saw an opportunity
in me, because my two ears were always
receptive to what you had to say,
like pages in a book you would have written

XX

if you'd only had the opportunity;
you had to fill them in that roundabout way
the very minute that you got the chance.
You were not sentimental or indulgent
in your dealings with me. When we read
William Ross or Alasdair MacDonald
together, I could not distinguish

XXI

in the echoing cavern of your mouth
the Gaelic syllables from the powerful
music that was natural to your voice.
You would become impatient and angry.
You didn't allow me to make mistakes.
Gentle spirit, my thanks go to you
even because of that impatience,

XIX

mhòir is 'na do phearsantachd, a rinn
ar cidsin beag a mheudachadh 's a sgaoileadh
nuair a bha thu nad shuidhe ann ar measg.
Chan fhac' thu annam ach cothrom,
      math dh'fhaodte,
do bhrìgh 's gu robh mo dhà chluais cho deiseil
an-còmhnaidh ris na chluinninn bhuat. Bha iad
mar dhuilleagan an leabhair a dh'iarr thu

XX

a sgrìobhadh, ach cha d' fhuair thu cothrom riamh,
is b' fheudar dhut an lìonadh, air an dòigh
fhiaraichte sin, cho luath 's a b' urrainn dhut.
Cha robh thu tairis no maoth-inntinneach
nad dhèiligeadh rium. Nuair a leughamaid
bàrdachd Mhic Mhaighstir Alasdair no Rois
le chèile, dh'fhairtlicheadh orm, ann an uamh

XXI

ath-aithriseach do bheòil, na fuaimean Gàidhlig
eadar-dhealachadh gu ceart bhon cheòl
neartmhor a bha nàdarrach nad ghuth.
Dh'fhàsadh tu feargach is neo-fhoigidneach.
Cha cheadaicheadh tu dhomh bhith mearachdach.
A spioraid chaoimh, seo mo bhuidheachas dhut
eadhon air sgàth na neo-fhoighidinn sin,

XXII

and not only because your nature was
courteous and open, full of humour,
and no one heard you complain about your state.
You didn't deal with me as with a stranger.
Although I was late in reaching you
we were given all the time we needed.
The effort that I made, when I was seeking

XXIII

proficiency, polishing and re-writing
verse would not seem vain, worthless to you.
I hope you wouldn't look on what I made
of what I got from you intolerantly
or with dissatisfaction. As you observed
my fun as well as my irreverence,
your laughter and delight would be awakened,

XXIV

encouraging me as I laboured with
subjects that aren't often spoken of.
Though we were not raised in the same language
my words for you today would sound clear
were you to hear them, because I made
a store of everything I gathered up
when we were together. Generous spirit,

XXII

's chan ann a-mhàin airson 's gu robh do ghnè
cùirteil an-còmhnaidh, fosgailte, làn àbhachd,
's nach cualas bhuat aon ghearan mu do staid.
Cha b' ann mar stràinnsear a dh'obraich thu leam.
Ged a bha mi fadalach gad ruighinn,
thugadh dhuinn ar n-ùine fhreagarach.
Na saothraichean a bh' agam, 's mise sireadh

XXIII

an sgil, a' lìomhadh rainn is ga ath-sgrìobhadh,
cha suarach, faoin a nochdadh iad fod shùil.
Cha b' ann le mi-riarachadh, tha mi 'n dòchas,
no le neo-fhulangas a shealladh tu
air na rinn mi leis na fhuair mi bhuat.
'S tu mothachadh dom spòrs is dom eas-urram,
dhùisgeadh do ghàir' is t' aoibhneas,
     tha mi smaointinn,

XXIV

bhiodh tu gam bhrosnachadh, 's mi dèiligeadh
ri cuspairean nach tric a bhruidhnear orr'.
Ged nach deach ar n-àrach an aon chànain,
's ann follaiseach a bhiodh mo chòmhradh air
do shon a-nis, is tu gam chluinntinn, oir
rinn mi tasgaidh dhe na chruinnich mi
nuair a bha sin còmhl'. A spioraid fhaoilidh,

XXV

if you are still a ghost, astray among
the other wandering shades, may these words find
their way to you as a frail ray of light
from this world of ours; or if you have
already been reborn, may they reach
you as a haunting memory that comes
unexpected, unexplained, unreasoned.

Budapest, June 2008

English translation by Niall O'Gallagher

XXV

tha mi dùraigeadh gum bi mo bhriathran
a' drùidheadh thugad, mas e taibhs' air faondradh
am measg nan taibhsean eil' a th' annad fhathast,
mar ghath de leus an t-saoghail seo a th' againn;
air neo, ma tha thu cheana air do bhreith
às ùr, gu ruig iad thu mar chuimhne aotrom,
's i tighinn ort gun dùil, gun chèill, gun reusan.

Budapest, san Ògmhios 2008

Jonathan Wonham

ALI BEN AM

There's no kind girl for Ali Ben Am there's no girl of his kind
for the gentle Ali Ben Am no girl of his imagination no girl
like his sister no girl like the mother of Ali Ben Am not like
the girl in the office the girl in the restaurant the girl at the
gym of Ali Ben Am but most of all not like the girl in the
posters the girl in the magazines the girl in the movies of
the bored Ali Ben Am wracking his brains thinking thinking
of every girl known unto him this Ali Ben Am searching
searching for one kind girl in the head of himself the head
he carries round on his shoulders the head where he finds
all along she was waiting for him the little face inside the
head of Ali Ben Am that one day is hardly there and then is
constantly there and speaks to him in dreams and asks him
why gentle Ali Ben Am is the movie watching Ali Ben Am
of expanding waist of life going to waste and so grows in the
mind of Ali Ben Am bigger and bigger Ali Ben Am bigger
and bigger Ali Ben Am must do something must contact
her must make a phone call must make a visit must make a
proposal and to the surprise of Ali Ben Am the phone call
pays off the visit pays off the proposal pays off and though
the distance of Ali Ben Am is real enough it does not seem
to turn her off the kind girl no longer in the head of Ali
Ben Am not quite the girl that was in the head not quite the
memory not quite the dream of Ali Ben Am but at least a girl
for Ali Ben Am and a girl for a wedding and a girl for a visa
and a girl for the contract signed by the hand of Ali Ben Am
the gentle shaking hand of Ali Ben Am who is living a dream
in his life who cannot wake up from the dream of the life of
Ali Ben Am from the life of the girl of Ali Ben Am who has
her own dream beyond the life of Ali Ben Am with the man
of her dreams who is already known to the girl of Ali Ben
Am who grows big in the empty days of the girl of Ali Ben Am
who must pop and pop again the bubble in her mind with
talk of breasts and silky skin in the computer of Ali Ben Am

who is not such a fool who collects the evidence who tries to save Ali Ben Am from the girl of the dreams of Ali Ben Am who revokes the familiarisation courses the visa the contract of the girl of Ali Ben Am who buys a return ticket who files a friendly severance who fights in court the martyred Ali Ben Am because even the mother even the sister of Ali Ben Am do not believe him when they hear the claims of the dream girl of Ali Ben Am the gentle Ali Ben Am he does not deserve this in his worst dream he does not deserve this the gentle Ali Ben Am.

DAWN DWYER

The big day fell on a Thursday and Thursday fell on Dawn Dwyer as she leant on the kitchen sideboard all of a clatter it fell the way a drawer of cutlery pulled out too far can fall except there was no cutlery there was no drawer there was just Dawn Dwyer by herself in the kitchen leant against the kitchen sideboard trying to resist Thursday falling on her trying to hold up Thursday as houses outside try to hold up their rooves and trees hold up their leaves and Dawn Dwyer was trying to leave and hold up her head she was trying to hold up her shoulders but Thursday was pushing down on her and disaster teetered like a drawer of cutlery a weight that was supported but to which point of being extended suddenly would fall and Dawn Dwyer was failing to hold up Thursday by herself against the kitchen sideboard tears rolling down her cheeks and falling onto the sideboard the way rain rolls down the window the way cars roll down the street the way Thursdays roll around for Dawn Dwyer supported but to which point the roof above her head the cutlery in the drawer the kitchen sideboard trying to resist as disaster teetered and the cars rolled down the street all going lopsided as she waited for the voice again with its note of command like a rattled drawer like a rattled sky Dawn Dwyer pushing down on the kitchen sideboard lifting her head and turning a little enough to see that he was standing blocking the light like a tree blocking the light a house blocking the light the voice with its note of command coming around suddenly asking what day did she think it was did she have any idea did she know it was Thursday Dawn Dwyer knew it was didn't need to be told it was wouldn't support it any longer wouldn't support another day wouldn't support this voice any longer Dawn Dwyer pulling the cutlery drawer all the way out letting the silver scatter across the floor the way leaves fall from the trees the way rain falls from the sky Dawn Dwyer felt the weight go felt the weight in her arms go followed her legs out into the light hall followed the hall out into the wet street Dawn Dwyer lifting her head to the scattering silver drops lifting her shoulders for the weight had dropped it might be any day it might be any week she didn't have a clue she didn't think of him she had no roof above her head there was no tree to block the light the silver drawer was empty now the empty cars rolled down the street the silver tears rolled down the cheeks of Dawn Dwyer.

DOUGLAS ARTHUR ROBERTS

Douglas Arthur Roberts feels he has waited long enough to
be with Hilda his wife now in the hands of God and waiting
for him in heaven as each morning Douglas Arthur Roberts
climbs out of bed and onto the shaky exercise bicycle closing
his eyes and imagining himself cycling down the road to
heaven as once Hilda and Douglas Arthur Roberts cycled
through a glen on a summer's honeymoony day of heather
bees and blue sky nowadays he's alone feeling slightly dizzy
sometimes hands a little numb Douglas Arthur Roberts has
some special gloves a special hat a special stick to see him
to the kitchen and since being normally a long time there
making a slice of toast the postie hands him his mail through
the kitchen window or makes a special sign to show there is
nothing today Douglas Arthur Roberts has nothing today
without Hilda who is waiting in heaven wondering what is
keeping him Douglas Arthur Roberts is keeping well perhaps
too well he used to have hot meals on wheels but now has
the frozen week's supply in the made-to-measure freezer to
be taken one a day making space for seven further meals
delivered Monday by white transit to the flat of Douglas
Arthur Roberts not quite big enough for the carpet in the
lounge not quite big enough for the bed in the bedroom
the bed which is now too big though sometimes he is not
alone she is next to him saying excitedly how it will be in
heaven like that day on the bicycle that day they first met
and Douglas Arthur Roberts tells Jack Duffy when they are
walking the block and Jack does not say a word who also was
once married but does not think of heaven much and can
and does do two more tours than Douglas Arthur Roberts
does also willing to accept frozen cod or hake most weeks
from Douglas Arthur Roberts his made-to-measure freezer
needing to be emptied carries it next door in plastic bags his
hands a little numb but feels he's helping someone Douglas
Arthur Roberts sits in the lounge with her rug over his knees

looking at her photograph the carpet turning at the skirting the shaky exercise bicycle hoping he will not be riding it tomorrow unless he is you-know-where.

LINDSEY LOMAS

The camera looms on Lindsey Lomas her flower print dress
a splash of fat a chart to show what each day Lindsey Lomas
takes on after finishing her family's scraps a few more saturated
grammes each day wrapped around a slim girl in a flower
print dress beside a riverbank the sound of children somehow
distant Lindsey Lomas seeming not to notice she is watching
a handsome man reading a book the supportive husband of
Lindsey Lomas somehow distant saying these changes might
not be much fun but he loves her for the next few weeks
each day the total contents of her stomach wrapped in a film
of fat shown to the viewers the inside facts in daily video
diaries Lindsey Lomas records her frank admissions laced
with commentary scraps while off screen Lindsey Lomas
somehow distant is still wrapped up in that scene the river
bank the handsome man the sound of children was it her the
girl with fat on her dress the same Lindsey Lomas who can't
change can't drop the act can't pretend any more all through
the unappreciated fact of her unhappiness Lindsey Lomas
seems in denial to spitting rashers to sundry scraps adding
to the fact that her weight and her family speak plainly of
another Lindsey Lomas now required to act before it is too
late in this scene which might even be an advert for low
cholesterol margarine saucepan in hand flower print dress
a splash of fat plainly seen through the camera's zoom lens
in the edited version on the stretched screen as one who no
longer seems like the slim Lindsey Lomas known from the
past who changes in front of her own family almost mistaken
near the end for someone else they can hardly believe she
reminds them of their mother before the unappreciated
fact of her unhappiness left off screen Lindsey Lomas now
exercising interest nationwide drops six sizes and drives to
the studio where in a bare room she changes in front of
her family the flower print dress stands like a child in her
mother's best the freshly pressed cotton between her fingers

against her back and stands alone before the camera a million eyes and only two eyes looking back along a riverbank the sound of children off screen a few scraps.

Rachel Woolf

THE GAITHERIN

Ease lowse a feebre o sailclaith
    whit flauchters abune steerage
Pirl twa-ply yairn o Shetland an merino fleeshes
Rive raivels frae denim overalls,
    droukit by the gowd-rush
Frae Paisley shawls, whit shaw the Fibonacci sequence
O Kashmiri teardribs, draw oot ane daizly threid
Tak warp an waft frae ilk o a faimily o tairtans
 Pouk a hundert thoosand blades
    o girse o the machair
Iver hauldin hail the synapses o fankelt ruits

Plett thegither whit haes been ingaithered
Tae mak a tensile twine
Mindin weel it niver fetters
Makin siccar it aye binds

THE GATHERING

Ease loose a fibre of sailcloth
    which flutters above steerage
Twist two-ply yarn of Shetland and merino fleeces
Pull strands from denim overalls,
    drenched by the gold-rush
From Paisley shawls, which show the Fibonacci sequence
Of Kashmiri teardrops, extract one dazzling thread
Take warp and weft from each of a family of tartans
Pluck a hundred thousand blades
    of grass of the machair
Minding well to keep intact the synapses of tangled roots

Wind together all that has been gathered
To make a tensile twine
Taking care it never fetters
Making sure it always binds

Catherine Wylie

OBJETS TROUVÉS

This year I found
pebbles, round and smooth, veined with quartz,
the carapace of a crab wrapped in green weed,
a curlew crying on the wind,
oystercatchers flying west to the Long Strand,
and the grey bars of waves shining like
        the back of a mackerel.
I wrapped them in sky cloth and
        posted them to the north.

Once delivered, they tumbled out
and your feet were washed in the Irish Sea,
your toes covered in emerald
and you were fed on the cream flesh of fish
caught on a line when the tide was high
and there was singing.

Keep them safe
on a windowsill, on your desk or in your pocket
so you may touch the shore again,
taste the salt on the wind
and hear the surf
for you are far away and inland.

BIOGRAPHIES

Patricia Ace's chapbook, *First Blood*, is published by Happen*Stance* Press. She also has six poems in *Booklight*, an anthology from Knucker Press (2009) and a Masters in Creative Writing from Glasgow University. She lives in Crieff, where she works part-time as a yoga teacher and creative writing tutor.

Dorothy Alexander has lived in the Scottish Borders all her life. For more details, see **www.dorothyalexander.co.uk**.

Kate Armstrong, a retired schoolteacher, lives in Dundee and writes poetry and prose, occasionally in Scots.

Jean Atkin lives with her family on a smallholding in Dumfriesshire and writes on a corner of the kitchen dresser. She won the Torbay Open Poetry Prize in 2009, and in 2010 the Ravenglass Poetry Press competition, judged by John Burnside, which will see a short collection of her work, *The Treeless Region*, published later this year.

Forbes Browne lives in Broughty Ferry. Born in Aberdeen, he was brought up in Cumbria, Yorkshire and Buckinghamshire, attended Aberdeen University then taught English in Dundee. He did little serious writing until his retirement. Broughty Ferry Environmental Project Eco-Poets Group and *Poetry Scotland* have published his work.

Tom Bryan: born in Canada in 1950, has been long-resident in Scotland, living now in Kelso. Widely published and broadcast poet, fiction and non-fiction writer. His work has appeared in previous *New Writing Scotland* anthologies. Currently the Royal Literary Fund Writing Fellow at the University of York.

A retired schoolteacher, in 2009 **E M Buchanan** completed a PhD in Creative Writing at Glasgow University. 'Agin

Mischefe' comes from the collection of poems and short stories, in English and Scots, backed by a commentary, reflecting aspects of her home ground in Angus on the east coast of Scotland.

John Burns, poet and short story writer, teaches English and Tai Chi. He is the author of *Celebration of the Light: Zen in the Novels of Neil Gunn* and *Series of Dreams: The Vision Songs of Bob Dylan*. His poetry appears in *Chuckies for the Cairn*.

Hazel Buchan Cameron has published four poetry pamphlet collections and another, *Finding IKEA,* is due out with Red Squirrel Press in 2010. Her pamphlet *The Currying Shop* was joint winner of the Callum Macdonald Memorial Award, 2008. She also writes stories and articles and is a member of *Lippy Bissoms.*

Chelsea Cargill, originally from Arbroath, lives in Edinburgh with her clunky old piano. She has been included in *Stand, Poetry Scotland* and *FuseLit*, and hopes her novella about her hometown will at some point meet the light of day. She also likes to write songs and soundtrack music. **www.succotash.org**

Jim Carruth was born in 1963 and grew up on his family's farm near Kilbarchan. His first collection, *Bovine Pastoral,* was published in 2004. Since then he has brought out a further two collections and an illustrated fable. In 2009 he was awarded a Robert Louis Stevenson Fellowship and was the winner of the James McCash poetry competition.

Alison Craig was born and miseducated in Birmingham, before moving to Scotland in 1981. She lives in Ayrshire with her artist husband and young daughter, and writes poetry, short fiction, articles and book reviews. Her work has been published in a number of magazines, and there's a novel on the back burner.

Morgan Downie is a poet, artist and cyclist. He works in healthcare. He believes the written word is magical. His first poetry collection, *Stone and Sea*, was published in 2010.

Colin Fraser lives in Edinburgh, where he once taught Philosophy and Artificial Intelligence. He edits the poetry magazine *Anon*.

Graham Fulton has been widely published in the UK and USA. His collections include *Knights of the Lower Floors* (Polygon), *This* (Rebel Inc), *Ritual Soup and other liquids* (Mariscat) and *Pocket Fugues* (CEP). A major collection *Open Plan* is to be published by Smokestack Books. He runs Controlled Explosion Press.

John Greeves is a poet, short story and feature writer. He has taught for over thirty years in Wales. He has been a part-time Creative Writing tutor for Cardiff University. His publications include *Unlocked* (Palores Publications, 2005) and *Almost a Doppelgänger* (Palores Publications, 2006). His new collection, *Cuba Libre*, will be published by Vanguard Press in 2010.

Rosemary Hector has had work published in magazines including *Chapman*, *Poetry Scotland*, *Gutter* and *New Writing Scotland*, and in anthologies published by Hodder, Lion, and Church House publishing. Recent experiments with prose have given her work a new sense of spaciousness and narrative impetus. She lives in Edinburgh.

Norman Kreitman, a retired physician living in Edinburgh, has written on aesthetics and the philosophy of literature, and to date has published three collections of poetry.

Alexander Lang, born in Aberdeen of seafaring stock, writes poetry and short fictions in solitary, where when his mind or his screen goes blank, he reminds himself of a quote from Aesop: 'Beware you lose the substance by grasping at the shadow.'

A former journalist, **Lis Lee** lives and writes in Kelso in the Scottish Borders. Her work has been published in several Scottish literary magazines and anthologies.

Linda McCann has published poetry and short stories, and has edited three anthologies of poetry and prose. She has been Creative Writing Fellow for the universities of Glasgow and Strathclyde, and has received a Hawthornden Fellowship and an Arts Council Award. She has honours degrees in English and Law.

After the long hard courtship of a novel, now consummated, **Patricia McCaw** has returned to her first love, poetry, where many of the offspring have been published in various publications. She has a Masters in Creative Writing from Edinburgh University, winning the Grierson Prize. She's pleased poetry is the new sex.

Stuart Robert Macdonald was brought up in south-west Scotland. He lives in Edinburgh with his wife and three children and works as a data librarian. He's been published widely in magazines and anthologies and is seeking a publisher for his first collection.

Ross McGregor lives and works in Kilmarnock, Ayrshire. He won Scottish Book Trust's New Writers Award in 2008 and took part in a mentoring programme for nine months. In this time he completed his first novel, *The Fair Fortnight*. He also writes poetry and short stories. He is currently writing his second novel.

Ann MacLaren lives in the beautiful village of Plockton in the north-west Highlands where she tries to find time out from a hectic social life for her writing. She has had articles and short stories published in various magazines, and has a PhD in Spanish and Portuguese Translation.

Hugh McMillan has published five full collections of

poetry, the latest being *Strange Bamboo* (Shoestring Press 2007) as well as several prizewinning pamphlets. Another full collection, *The Lost Garden*, is due in 2010. He lives in Penpont in Dumfries and Galloway.

Kona Macphee grew up in Australia and now lives in Crieff, Scotland. She has published two collections with Bloodaxe, *Tails* (2004) and *Perfect Blue* (2010). *Tails* is now being sold to raise money for UNICEF, and *Perfect Blue* includes a free companion e-book of commentaries – see **www. konamacphee.com** for more.

Jason Monios lives in Edinburgh. His publications include *Acumen, Poetry Scotland, New Writing Scotland, Horizon, nthposition, Umbrella* and *The Guardian*.

Theresa Muñoz was born in Vancouver and now lives in Edinburgh. Her work has appeared in *Poetry Scotland, The Red Wheelbarrow, Canadian Literature, Echolocation* and many others. She has won the Kirkpatrick Dobie Award as well as the Norman Rothstein Award for Poetry. She is working on her first collection, *Everything I Know Up To Now*.

Donald S Murray is a weaver's son from Ness, Isle of Lewis who now lives and works in Shetland. Among other works, he is the writer of *Small Expectations* (Two Ravens Press) and *The Guga Hunters* (Birlinn). A Gaelic speaker, he is also partial to the taste of young gannet.

John Murray stays in Kelso. He teaches landscape architecture at Edinburgh College of Art. Poetry is in *Chapman, Lallans, The Eildon Tree* and *New Writing Scotland*. Diehard published *Chiaroscuro* in 2001. A collection of poems with images by John McGregor about the River Teviot can be found in *Tweed Rivers*.

Niall O'Gallagher works from Holyrood as a political reporter for the BBC. In 2009 he was awarded a New Writers Award by the Scottish Book Trust / Comhairle nan Leabhraichean to work on a collection of poems. Niall has written for magazines and newspapers including *The Guardian* and *The Herald*. He lives in Glasgow.

Catherine Orr-Frier grew up in Glasgow where she trained as a physiotherapist. Marriage took her sojourning across central Scotland. At the age of fifty she was amazed to find herself writing and performing poetry and being published. She now lives in Glasgow with her second husband and has three children and five grandchildren.

Jane Patience has published short stories and poetry, and has written for radio. She finds inspiration in travel and the people and sounds of Scotland. Currently living in north Glasgow with her family and a large collection of waterproof gear; she aspires to complete her first novel this year.

Water Perrie grew up in 1950s Lanarkshire. Educated Edinburgh and Stirling. Numerous collections of poetry, a travel book on Eastern Europe and critical pamphlets. Sometime teacher of philosophy. Joint editor of *Fras* magazine. Lives in Dunning, Perthshire. His new *Lyrics and Tales in Twa Tongues* appears later this year.

Wayne Price was born in south Wales and now teaches at the University of Aberdeen. He has published short stories and poems in many anthologies and journals in the UK, Ireland and America and has been a prizewinner in a number of international fiction and poetry competitions.

A P Pullan: coloured in by Yorkshire, now settled in Ayrshire. Works as a teacher for pupils with special educational needs. Poems previously in *Iota* and *Poetry Scotland*.

Tracey S Rosenberg has spent much of her life working in independent bookshops, and recently became Booksales

Officer at the Edinburgh International Book Festival. She's had poems published in *Chapman* and online at the Human Genre Project, and captains a convincingly successful team at the Blackwell Book Quiz.

Karin Slater is a 26-year-old Creative Writing graduate based in the Outer Hebrides. She's had a number of poems printed in small press publications, and when not writing she currently splits her time between a bespoke weaving company and a peat-sodden allotment.

Michael Stephenson was born in 1980 and lives in Bathgate, West Lothian. He has had poems published in a number of Scottish magazines such as *Poetry Scotland* and *The Red Wheelbarrow*, and is working towards a first collection.

Gerda Stevenson (actor/writer/director): poetry and prose published in *Scotsman, Cencrastus, Eildon Tree, Chapman, Markings, Parnassus: Poetry in Review, Cleave* (Two Ravens Press), *Edinburgh Review, New Writing Scotland, Aesthetica Magazine*; awarded SAC writer's bursary, 2008; stage play *Federer Versus Murray* produced at Òran Mór, 2010; her many BBC Radio 4 dramatisations include *The Heart of Midlothian* and *Sunset Song*. **www.gerdastevenson.co.uk**

Jim Stewart was born in Dundee in 1952. He teaches Creative Writing with Kirsty Gunn at the University of Dundee, and also teaches literature part-time there and in St Andrews University. Poems by him have appeared recently in *For A' That* (an anthology honouring Burns), *InterLitQ* and *Gutter*.

Judith Taylor lives in Aberdeen. Her poetry has appeared in a number of magazines: her first chapbook collection, *Earthlight*, was published by Koo Press (2006) and her second, *Local Colour*, by Calder Wood Press (2010). She has appeared at Shore Poets, StAnza, and at the Durham Book Festival. **www.secondlightlive.co.uk/members/judithtaylor.shtml**

Valerie Thornton is a writer, an editor and a Creative Writing tutor. She has held two Royal Literary Fund Writing Fellowships at Glasgow University. Her latest creative-writing textbooks are *The Writer's Craft*, and *The Young Writer's Craft* (Hodder Gibson). Her second collection of poems from Mariscat Press is imminent.

Ryan Van Winkle is currently the Reader in Residence at the Scottish Poetry Library. His poems have appeared in *The American Poetry Review*, *AGNI* and *Northwords Now*. He is the curator of The Golden Hour – a monthly literary cabaret based at the Forest Arts Collective in Edinburgh.

Fiona Ritchie Walker is from Montrose, Angus, now living south of the border in Blaydon, near Newcastle. She is the author of two poetry collections, *Lip Reading* and *Garibaldi's Legs*, plus the chapbook, *Angus Palette*. Her work is also published in magazine and anthologies, including the British Council's *New Writing*.

Christopher Whyte is a prize-winning poet in Gaelic and the author of four novels in English. His third collection, *Dealbh Athar*, was published by Coiscéim of Dublin, and a fourth collection in Gaelic and English, *Bho Leabhar-Latha Maria Malibran / From the Diary of Maria Malibran* by Acair of Stornoway, in 2009. He lives in Budapest and writes full-time.

Jonathan Wonham was born in Glasgow in 1965. He works as an exploration geologist in Norway. Publications include the book *Poetry Introduction 7* (Faber) and numerous magazines and anthologies including *New Writing Scotland 21*. A poetry collection entitled *Steel Horizon: North Sea Poems* is forthcoming from Incline Press.

Rachel Woolf lives in North Berwick. She was runner-up in The Gathering poetry competition 2009. 'The Stuff o Folk' is in the 2nd National Galleries of Scotland *Inspired?*

Get Writing! anthology and 'Seasoning' is published on-line by *qarrtsiluni*. Rachel composes lullabies and has produced pocket chapbooks of some longer pieces.

Originally from Cheshire, **Catherine Wylie** was educated at the University of Aberdeen. For a number of years she has lived in the Stirling area and taught English.